Jamila's

HILLTOP PRIMARY SCHOOL

Written by Jillian Powell

Illustrated by Samantha Woo

RISING ★ STARS

The Sultan must pick a Sultana.

Jamila must pass a rest test.

They stuff the softest felt mattress.

Next, they fluff up six velvet quilts.

Jamila jumps on a box to get into bed.

The sun is up. Jamila did not rest.

She felt a bump in the bed.

It is just a speck of dust!

Jamila is glad to pass the test.

She will be the best Sultana!

Talk about the story

Ask your child these questions:

1 Why did Jamila want to pass the rest test?

2 How many velvet quilts were there?

3 How did Jamila get into the bed?

4 Why didn't Jamila get a good night's rest?

5 What does your bedding look like?

6 Would you like your bed to look like Jamila's?

Can your child retell the story using their own words?